DUNES Review

**Our cover art, entitled "Welcome to my World,"
is by Traverse City artist Nancy Adams Nash.**

Acrylic on wood panel 20" x 20" 2015, image courtesy of the artist.

DUNES REVIEW

Volume 25 Issue 1

Spring 2021

CONTENTS

Editors' Notes

Like everyone else, we at the *Dunes* have been affected by these [insert overused descriptor] times. This issue, 25.1, began as 24.2. Everything took longer. And no wonder. But here we are, with a lovely issue to share with you, courtesy of everyone's efforts and continued good faith. Working with authors to get their stories and poems just right is pure pleasure. Our new cracking production editor, Kelli, is a wonder. And Nancy Adams Nash's painting "Welcome to My World" captures for me one of the motifs running through the work. We found ourselves selecting work that addressed transformation—the need for which is sometimes born of difficult or, dare we say, compressed, situations. Like these times. Reading submissions, I feel certain that the making and sharing of art is a fundamental and necessary act of spirit and survival. My spirits were buoyed, not only by the contents but also by the process itself of shaping this little journal. Nash's painting and the work in this issue remind me that there is something in us that wants a larger view, that will build ladders, that will climb out of ourselves in order to have a good look around at the stars. I hope you enjoy the view.

— *Teresa Scollon*

Depending on where you're sitting, you may feel like 2020 flew by. Or you might feel like it dragged on forever—that the essence of the past year lives on, even after the calendar flipped, even now that the crocuses are braving a new season. Somehow it also feels like both of those things are true simultaneously: twelve months have been both eternal and a finger-snap. *You appear to arrive somewhere, only to find yourself back at the starting point,* says Sara Dallmayr. And Moira Walsh's riptide ushers us back to the same beach we left behind—*Although / of course / not the same.*

Contradictions coexist gracefully in this issue, as they do in our lives. Certainty dances alongside paradox. Trapped in the icebox of quarantine, we discover—or eschew—new sources of contentment. We learn to articulate our own needs while also grappling with our individual insignificance in the grand scheme. We look back on an unprecedented year and step forward hopefully, but then again, *What do we know of deer or deer tracks or certainty or others?*

— *Jennifer Yeatts*

Moira Walsh

WAKING UP CLOSE TO YOU

The snow hides the road
I don't want to change a thing

Billy Thrasher
TWO-LANE HIGHWAY

Your head was on   the flying cat pillowcase
when you rolled over,   while lying on the futon,
plain-smiled at me,   felt my cheek
                                               with padded hand,
blinked,   then turned   to the wall

with the paint outline of the shelf
                              that fell the year before.

The sun shone   through the blinds
forming slits on a picture;   splitting souls
                                             of a family.

I'm a hitchhiker   picked up   for a small span
                                          of preparation.

I stand up,   you stand   on the futon,
reach your arms for   me   to hold you;

remember   that I did.

Leah Christianson
IS THAT WHAT YOU THINK?

After I move north, I begin dreaming that the house has frozen into a giant ice cube. When our house actually does get blockaded by a freak ice storm, my first thought is: I should have listened. My second is: I should have gone grocery shopping. I yank on the front door's handle. Pull with all my weight. I tell the door to fuck off. It stays firmly fucked. Then, because I've never been trapped inside my own house, I call my neighbors for suggestions regarding escape.

Myra, the sweet grandma who lives across the street, laughs at me.

I open up the blinds. Ice is thickening around the house into a perfect cube.

"Do you have a pickaxe?" I ask, mostly kidding.

"Oh, honey," she says. "You wouldn't know the first thing about using that."

"This can't be actually happening."

"Well, I do have an axe," says Myra.

Where am I? The grandmothers have weapons and the houses are impenetrable.

"But I can't get to you either, honey. Look."

I look. The ice is making the world all wobbly. Usually, it's a place of trying-too-hard-greens and perma-gray-skies and carbon-copy-houses, where I live with my boyfriend, Ned, who knows the quickest route to every chain restaurant and how to get a discount on firewood. Now, little spiderweb cracks run through ice encasing my home. Myra's place has grizzled itself into a blob and is getting harder to see by the second. My phone says that it is Tuesday morning.

"I'm looking but I can't see."

"I'm stuck too," says Myra.

"What do you think we should do?" I ask, mostly serious.

"Honey," she says, laughing again. "Not a damn thing."

I hang up the phone. The roof wheezes out a chuckle. Maybe more of a guffaw. Maybe the roof and Myra are in cahoots.

"You think you scare me?" I ask the roof. I'm teasing—I like this house. We picked it out together, before I moved. I wanted to live here instead of the place closer to Ned's work, because I thought this house could be made homey. When I arrived, homey-making commenced. We stripped the floors and I painted the walls autumn colors and Ned cleaned the windows I couldn't reach. We got an old cat named Tito with an undisclosed thyroid tumor that made bowel control rather difficult. Ned didn't want him, but I thought he'd make for good company.

"You're good company," said Ned. "And you don't shit on my carpet."

Tito must have sensed this because he ran away two weeks ago, just before our Midwest temperatures dipped to levels unsuitable for humans. Or, as Ned puts it, "things got a little chilly."

I try the back door, then the front again. I wiggle and cajole. I give good kicks, just to be sure. Neither of them allows for a break on through to the other side.

"Missed opportunity," I tell the doors.

Well, today doesn't have to be a total loss. I work from home as a medical claims processor, so this doesn't have to derail my day. Not that work ever derails my day—it's the kind of job I can squeeze into the nooks of other plans. That was Ned's main argument when the time came for one of us to move to the other. We had been doing long distance since college, and when my role was transitioned to "remote work only," it made sense. It comes in handy on days when one is frozen into one's house. And if Ned's stuck here, too, I'll get a day with him. He's been working so much I've barely seen him.

I go to the little bedroom we use as an at-home office.

"Having an ice day?" I call as I swing the door open. But my voice dies in empty corners. I am alone.

Confused, I call him.

"Where are you?"

"Work. Why?" Ned's voice is crisp. He's a fan of strong verbs and short sentences.

"Uh…how did you get out?"

"Out of what?"

"The house…"

"How did I get out of the house? That's what you're calling to ask?"

I look outside again, wanting more evidence of what's been proving itself all morning.

"Yes. That's what I'm asking. Because, see, I'm frozen into the house. I can't get out."

"What?"

"I realize how this sounds. But. I am. Stuck in. The house."

"Are you sure you can't force the door open?"

"I don't think you're grasping what I'm saying here. The house is an ice cube."

"Ok. Well." I hear him typing. A nearby phone rings. "I don't know what to say. I've never heard of anything like that."

"What time did you leave this morning? This looks really thick. You must have been up before—"

"Listen, Char, I've got a ton on my plate today. I'll be home around eight. Do you need me?"

He says my name differently than everyone else. Usually, Charlotte gets shortened to Shar. But Ned, in all his particularity, must adhere to phonetics. To him, I'm Char. As in the Arctic fish. As in what coal does.

"You have food? Heat?" he asks.

"Yes. Well, not much food."

"Didn't you go yesterday? Isn't Monday grocery day?"

I blink at the phone a few times. "When's the last time you went shopping?"

Ned keeps on typing, saying nothing. Human buzz surrounds him. I hear coffee pouring into chipped mugs, hushed gossips between friends a few desks over, a radio playing a morning show with too many sound effects. I press the phone harder against my cheek.

"It's fine," I say. "It's warm inside. I called Myra."

"Oh good," he says, sounding very far away. "Myra."

"She didn't seem to find this strange. Do you?"

"What?"

"Find it strange?"

I am still squinting out the window. Ice fades from white to gray to an impossible blue. Somewhere outside, or maybe inside the thickness—my depth perception is warped—something is trapped.

"Well," Ned is saying, snapping me back inside. "I really don't think there's anything I can do right now. I'll figure something out on my way home from work. Okay?"

I wonder if Tito is all right. I think about bringing him up, just to say something else.

"Fine," I say. "See you around eight. If I haven't popsiclized by then."

"I thought you said it was warm."

"I—never mind. Yes, it's warm."

"Ok," says Ned, keyboard crackling away. "See you."

The phone beeps his goodbye. I'm still trying to figure what's outside the window. When I lean closer, my breath heats up the glass, making the view a bit clearer.

It's a bird. It's far away, but once I've recognized the shape, it's unmistakable. Its wings are at uneven planes, as if it got trapped mid-flight. As if it broke its body trying to escape. I close the blinds but can still see it, hanging there. The roof makes a sound like a woman who doesn't care who hears her.

My mother was worried when I moved here.

It's not that I don't like Ned, she told me. He's great, she reiterated. I'm just worried about you. Meeting people isn't easy if—what was the phrase she used? If you don't have somewhere to plug in.

I said things like: I'll have Ned. He has friends. This makes the most sense. I work from home, so this is the easiest option.

She knew, she knew.

"But Charlotte, sweetie, that's what I'm afraid of."

When I asked why, she said: "It just sounds so isolating."

We didn't really talk about it after that. I think about calling her, making this story into a joke. But I don't think she'll find it funny.

Where she lives now, it's sparkly and humid and rolling on flat forever. People drive trucks with opinions and wear sunglasses all year round. I call Myra instead.

"Hiya, Char," she says before I announce myself. Char as in sharp. Char as in shart.

"How you holding up?" she continues.

"The roof is making strange noises."

"Oh, it's just settling," she says.

"Doesn't ice expand?"

"Oh. I think so."

"Myra," I say, opening and closing the pantry. Cans of cat food sit on the bottom shelf. Tuna, chicken. Undefined meats. "Could anything survive this?"

"We're still kicking, aren't we?"

I nod at the phone.

"How is this possible?" I ask. "Scientifically speaking?" Myra laughs like she's never been lonely.

"Scientifically? You're loony, honey! A real loon." She makes a cooing noise into the phone.

"What's that?" I ask.

"A loon call," says Myra, like I'm the old bird here. "Where's Nedley? Isn't he there with you?" she asks when she stops looning.

"No," I say. "He's not."

"Well, don't worry about it. This isn't so bad. This snow doesn't know what it's doing. The ice, on the other hand, is very sure of itself."

That sounds bad to me, but what do I know?

"It's snowing, too?"

"Can't you see it?"

I look out.

"No," I say. "Can't see a thing."

I return to the office. It's dark but warm, like somewhere deep underground. Ned's desk is so tidy. There's a little picture of us at Lake Superior in the left corner and a neat pile of documents labeled "CONFIDENTIAL" in front of it. On the right side, a steampunk lamp and a coaster, ready to illuminate coffee cups and bright ideas. Pens stands at attention, equidistant from one another, ready for duty.

"He's a meticulous boy, isn't he?" my mother said the first time she met him.

I call but hang up after two rings. My phone tells me that I'm late for a meeting to review a new release of ICD-10 codes. Calls like this usually involve one person whining on for hours without pausing for questions or even a "Hey, how's the weather up there?" They're emptier than this house. I put the phone back in my pocket.

Once, in college, Ned brought me home for Christmas. We drove to a lake near his parents' house. On the map, the shoreline gnarled around like a ginger root. In person, it looked a lot smaller than I expected. But then it just kept going. Ned pulled off the road, wiggled his eyebrows, then drove out onto the ice. I started screaming.

We stopped in the middle of the lake, parking next to a line of pickup trucks and some little huts. There was even an RV. First, I was afraid to get out of the car. Then, I was afraid to stay in it. Stepping onto the ice, I held onto the door, expecting slickness to send me to my butt. But it felt like solid ground—bumpy, a little dirty.

Ned laughed as I clung to the car. The sky was the color of dull pearls. His teeth matched. Ned bent over to rub a gloved hand across the ice, dusting off the thin layer of snow.

"See? It's frozen three feet thick, at least."

"How can you tell?"

He shrugged, looked down. "See that color?"

"What color?"

"Exactly."

What a smartass he was. I threw snow at him without putting gloves on. My fingers went red, then white, then yellow. He breathed onto my hands, gave me his gloves, then unzipped his coat so I could wrap my arms around his warm, warm body. I could see our life together then, as his breath puffed little clouds above my head. The life we would build together.

It's almost three in the afternoon. This is normally the time I would take a break from work—make some tea, go for a walk if the weather allowed. When Tito was here, he'd beg for early dinner. I'd ask him whether he thought undefined meats would go to his gut or his hips. He would meow dismissively or poop in the hallway. We'd keep it fresh, Tito and I. But then I realize: I haven't done any work today.

"Oops," I say.

Oh God, make it stop, the roof groans back.

I call Ned again. It goes to voicemail.

"Hi, it's me. It is three p.m. and I wanted you to know that I am still a living, breathing human. Things are fine here. The roof is making weird noises. But. We're all fine here. Ha. Okay, bye. Love you."

I go back upstairs. Outside the front window, that bird is still frozen. Is it closer? There are lines in its feathers that I didn't notice before.

I lie down on the kitchen floor, placing my feet up on the sink's lip.

Get off, says the sink.

"Don't mouth off," I tell the sink.

Don't talk to her like that, says the roof.

I apologize to the sink.

"I just apologized to a sink," I tell the air. We keep it fun, the house and I.

I told you it would be lonely, says my mother.

And then I just lie there.

He calls back after six.

"I'm leaving soon. Weather's getting bad here."

"Oh, is it? Is the weather bad?"

"Yes," he says. "I just said that."

"How did you get out of the house?" I ask. I have to know.

Ned sighs. "I just walked out. I don't know. It must have gotten worse after I left."

Of course. He just walked out. He knows how to navigate here, so the house just lets him go. Me, on the other hand. This is all the room I get.

"I moved here for you," I say. I left a place of polka-dotted hills and mismatched bridges and every fusion food imaginable, where people flooded conversations with unfathomable plans and made me feel as interchangeable as a side order at T.G.I. Friday's. "And I am frozen into the house."

"Yes," he says. "I am aware of that, Char. We will figure it out."

Char, as in scorched.

"Where do I fit?"

"What?"

"Is this our life, or do I need to buy my own axe?"

"I don't know how to respond to that. We've been on the phone for fifty-three seconds."

"Come home," I say and hang up.

I keep lying there. The phone rings and I let it go. I lie and lie. It rings and rings. When I used to let the phone ring like this, Tito would sit on it. I think the vibrations felt good on his thyroid. Eventually, I answer.

"Checking in on ya, hon," says Myra. "Is Ned home yet?"

"No," I say, still staring at the ceiling. I imagine a crack starting small, spreading quickly. "How long will this last?"

"Who knows? As long as you let it, I guess."

"Oh, so this is up to me now."

Myra pauses.

"I'm simply trying to be decent, honey," she says, sounding a little wobbly. Foamy guilt bubbles up. For all her joking—maybe because of it—I haven't asked Myra how she's doing today. Not once. When I start to speak, she chuckles.

"What a lark," she says. "I'm not simple or decent."

I'm about to tell Myra that she's the best friend I've got when she says, "Oh, that's the door," and hangs up.

Ten minutes later, something scratches at the lock. Ned appears. Snow dusts his collar and exhaustion droops his face.

"How did you get in?"

"What?" asks Ned, dropping his briefcase on the ground and walking across the threshold. He stands above me, looking almost imposing. Like a statue that's cut itself shaving.

"I just walked in, Char. Come on, let's get out of the house. Why don't I take you to dinner? Wherever you want."

"Don't do that. I have been trapped. And you just waltz in the door. Like I'm. Like. You know."

He scrunches his eyebrows together and reaches his arm down. I lift my arms toward him but don't take his hand.

"I'm stuck," I say.

He pulls me to my feet in one powerful yank. My legs feel waterlogged—I latch my arms around his waist to keep from tumbling back down. He grabs back. He puts his thumb under my chin and gently tilts my head backwards. Snow melts in his hair, loosing some strands across his forehead. When we met, he was just a kid. Now, look.

"Is that what you think?" he asks.

Lauren Claus
BACKYARD

The risk of runoff. Residue
     from each storm last winter.
He said yes, he is leaving.
      Light follows the leaves
down, and they loosen into sediment.
     When he said yes, keep the house,
she knew keep means *to celebrate,*
     solemnize — not *to maintain.*
Not to own. It is Sunday,
     so dark there are no shadows.
There is too much to remember here.
     As if the river is not swollen,
she slips in. As if he will fix the overflow.
     The old gate. The broken window,
its irrevocable light.

Scott Dorsch
RED/PURPLE/WHITE

Today we wake to scratches of ice
     at the window, hail breaking willows.
It's brown-sugar oatmeal with an egg on top and
     a dose of cowboy cleaner:
hot coffee and the gray scrapings of the bowl.
     Snow wings sideways, sounds like bees.
Radio hisses by the sink, sounds like bees.
     We posthole to the barn, find a manger scene
of goats sleeping late, tuck-kneed
     in a line. We feather hay in wire feeders
then busy ourselves with sledding,
     putting off the forever dirt of
the garden, the forever loose teeth of the fence line.
     We look for mountains that aren't there.

Then, a scream, a rough whip of wind.
     Then, we're running, astronauts in full
moonscape-carom down the hill.
     With flashlights we find the screams.
Two goats, Pegs and Ballet, in the milk parlor,
     sideways in the dirt, pulsing—orange,
horned heads pushing out from under their tails.
     The stink of sour milk, the red/purple/
white slosh of life. Wind tugs
     at the roof. We hold down the walls.

The snow will melt. We'll bury
     the placenta by the plum tree.
Low on hay, grass gone to snow, we'll
     follow the creek, snip pinky-wide whips of red
willow into fodder. The kids will be taken,
     named Zeus and Pirouette, and be fed
soy formula from stove-warm bottles.
     Ballet will learn the spinal pressure
of a kick-bar, the tussle of calloused hands
     feeding from her udder. We'll

make five dollars from a quart of milk,
        still warm.

But for now we watch the spindrift in the parlor,
        the amniotic rivulets rushing dirt around
two kids born side by side. In seconds,
        miraculously, they lift onto prune-sized
hooves and probe cold air for an udder. They're
        met instead by thick tongues,
by their mothers. The moon sifts past
        lacey clouds and slats, the pine joists rattle.
In dirt, we laugh, we hug, we kneel, we shake:
        we have nothing, we have everything.

Erin Wilson
FIELD GUIDE

There are times I wish my ignorance were more complete.

--Robert Hass

You're working your foot
into your right snowshoe
not sveltly, just plunk
and push, then a little further,
the only way you know how,
when you hear him near you.
Then up she comes over the
snowbank behind him, a regulated
swish, swish, closing itself off
like a peanut back into its shell.

They inform you of two things,
you who didn't ask. One,
they've just seen a grouse.
To which you insert, as you
finagle your foot into
the snowshoe's strappings,
"Oh yes, they've been active lately,
maybe nibbling early buds
in treetops." And two,
there's been no deer activity lately.
They gloat, "We know
where they tend to go."
Huh. You too, you guess,
but you don't say so.
You look up instead.
Their saying things
somehow bites you.

Then off you all go,
they to wherever, and you
to round all of the park trails,
well worked for the first,

easy third, then less well,
then not at all, except for
where you waded through
with great effort last week,
and even these prints have mostly
been filled in again by flurries
and wind-swept snow.

While you walk you replay
the few sentences exchanged,
noting where the wildlife enthusiasts'
tracks end (by the end of the first third).
So, they know where the deer
tend to go, eh?
But this reworking of words
is toxic and what you hate more
than their contribution, is your own.
What the hell do you really know
about grouse behaviour?
Nothing but bits you've observed
during leisure over years of strolling.

You think back on a talk you watched,
E. O. Wilson and Robert Hass
chatting it up about the intersection
of art and science. You don't remember
anything in particular said,
but jesus-god you recall
Hass's demeanour,
how he sat back excited
and listened,
acquiescing and inviting.
Not for a single second
did you think he knew less,
but he was eager for any moment
that might flash true and startle.

Ask more, you coax yourself
as you practice foot pacing and cadence,
for nothing has been a better authority for you than:

one, the elderly couple
you proudly came upon years before
when returning from a particularly long jaunt
— you yearned for their prompt so that you could
boast about how far you'd run —
but they'd assumed you'd gone much, much farther;

two, the wet granite ledge you slipped from
in the woods, alone last spring;

three, your lying lovers
and your lies to them;

and/or four, aberrant cells.

What do you know about deer or
deer tracks or certainty or others?

Theresa Monteiro
ON MARTYRDOM

Nice is not a virtue —
a grumpy professor says.
Everyone's buying chocolates
on account of Valentine who was
beheaded for love. He says,
anyone can be sweet
for a price. I ask:
What about the brutal February
of your life? What about loneliness
and doubt, forgetting to
look into mirrors and say:
Yes, I am dull,
shrinking, and still love. Because,
what if (since we have only
one word for it) you look
and find a love of comfort — or worse, a love
of admiration? What if you have no
burned-at-the stake kind of love? What if
you fall asleep reading Hass and dream
you're reading Hass? The words on the page end
and the white page disappears
somewhere to your left, and of course,
the poems aren't really
his. Maybe they're yours but you won't
remember them when you wake. You wake
remembering you have memorized almost nothing —
you write poems on recycled paper.
You touch the triangle of arrows and understand
the paper used to have different words (in its last life)
words like *Lambchops* and *Palmolive*,
outlined in black dashes to show women where to cut,
how to save. American cheese is so much a pound —
with the coupon, so much less.
The cheese is dyed yellow, just
like your paper was
before it was poetry, but after

it was a tree dropping its leaves for us
to rake up and squash into paper bags and the professor says,
raking is not a virtue either, it's just control.
Blow the leaves into the woods
and do something hard. Which is easy
to say, until you look in the mirror,
smiling, and find you are
the mother possum, all ten babies
hanging from your fur—you're foraging,
finding the pit
of an apricot with flesh
still clinging.

Keith Grimes
THE END OF THE MARSH

We walk along the rough wooden planks of the boardwalk trail
that spans the Arcadia Marsh Nature Preserve. The planks form an
ordered walkway over the shallow water, through stands of trees and
across small meadows, and guide us through various ecosystems.
Small green signs posted along the path point out the local species of
flora and fauna. The July sun scorches overhead and the air shimmers
with humidity just above the water. The birds are not as lively at
midday as at daybreak or sunset, but the display of teeming life
around us doesn't disappoint. We walk this peaceful path because we
need a reset after last night.

I take the lead, my wife beside me, since I am the more avid bird
enthusiast. She is more enthralled by what is occurring under the
duckweed-covered surface of the marsh, eager to spot a family
of painted turtles or a school of sculpins. Her ears perk up at the
"gullup" of a wary bullfrog hidden beneath a thick stand of stinging
nettles, while I stand mesmerized by the acrobatic dance of tree
swallows feeding on insects in erratic flight patterns. They dart
left then right, quickly gaining altitude, then dropping just as fast,
changing directions on a whim.

Michigan marshes are accustomed to loss. Over eighty percent
of the Great Lakes coastal marshes have been lost to man-made
development. This Arcadian jewel is now one of only sixteen coastal
marshes that remain in Michigan. A combination of marsh and sedge
meadow, the preserve stands at approximately 300 acres and is home
to over 250 bird species, 200 plant species, and nearly 30 fish species.
It persists thanks to the conservation efforts of the Grand Traverse
Regional Land Conservancy. I feel the vibrancy of this place in my
bones, its will to survive against all odds. I look at my wife and I want
to fight for what we still have.

We hold hands as we walk down the path. A stiff breeze blows across
the lake and nearly takes her hat with it. We laugh after spotting
another hat already embedded in a solitary stand of blooming

arrowheads, a previous catch by the plucky bluster. I marvel aloud at the cloudless azure dome above us, encircling us, touching down at the far corners of the verdant earth. She echoes my wonderment.

Farther along the path, we encounter a mating pair of mute swans floating along a hidden current in the water. Their snow-white plumage and fiery orange beaks offer no camouflage against our prying eyes. They are alone, separated from the other swans, and we wonder aloud if this is normal behavior. Are they a gregarious species like other birds, or do they actively prefer their solitude? I typically prefer solitude and enjoy separating from the group, while my wife is gregarious and outgoing, much like the red-winged blackbirds hovering and calling over the cattails. They appear to float on the wind, then dive toward the lower tree branches in screaming packs, chittering and chirping.

I wrap my arm around her waist and pull her close. She doesn't resist and I am relieved. This marsh is a respite for the many species of birds that travel through it. It's calm and inviting, welcoming travelers into nature's bosom. We are caught up in it, like the birds, without worry about tomorrow. No talk of divorce, not in this moment. A green heron passes overhead, squeaking out a honk as it settles into the upper branches of a dead elm tree. Its handsome green feathers sparking in the sunlight give life back to a tree long dead.

A stunning stand of Allegheny monkeyflower spreads out before us with its blue and purple petals, like some opulent Persian carpet unfurling to the horizon. It reaches out across the marsh, touching land far off to the east. Amid the flowers sprout several caches of purple bull thistle. Goldfinches flock to feed on the thistle seeds, a stunning display of canary-yellow flitting about the purple landscape. These birds, so energetic and vibrant, personify joy. I quietly thank God for this moment.

Suddenly we reach the end of the marsh path and she says she wants to talk. We watch in silence as the swans take flight, low over the marshy lake, but gradually gaining altitude over the trees. They disappear into the clouds. I don't want to talk, but I keep that to myself. I would prefer to hold this moment before us, to revel in the small miracles occurring everywhere in the remote recesses of the marsh. I don't want this to end.

A pair of monarch butterflies hover around us, their flight intertwined in a beautiful spiraling dance. Their orange and black wings blaze in the afternoon sun. This marsh will gently lull as the day cools and the sun sets over Lake Michigan. Tomorrow, it will begin its cycle anew. Suddenly, the butterflies part and flutter off to different parts of the marsh. I wonder if they will find each other again. Perhaps they have done all that they came here to do.

Diana Arnold
CARPENTER

Pat me down, partner.

Bring your tools, noble carpenter.

Slide your hands
over my corners.
Smooth, you
round them
and add
pressure
to remove
my past dust
with your finger

behold – !
my original molding.

Then,
take a breath in
look me in the eyes
and tell me
what you can build
with
what you are holding.

David Capps
BLUE-GREEN SIJO

Stay, calamitous blue, called dawn's thought rising up through
miles of sky, I have inched through mud and bone to find you,
over lichen, wet-green slopes, a child hiding from his father.

Stay, calamitous blue, called dawn's thought rising up through
miles of sky, I have inched through mud and bone to find you,
over lichen, wet-green slopes, words in other languages green.

Stay, miles of sky, over lichen. Think all the languages green.

Erin Wilson
CERTAINTY

We see three herons.

Or two herons, one twice.

Or one heron, three times.

Marcus Whalbring
PLASTIC BAG CAUGHT IN A TREE

It makes me not see the tree.
The wind flagging it makes me
not hear the wind.
It's grey and pillowy and full of rain
like a cloud, but it's not a cloud.
The tree didn't go shopping for air
but when the leaves come back in spring
some will need a price check on breathing.
I didn't put it up there, but
I feel like I put it up there.
I don't drink from rivers
but I drink from rivers. There's a river
in my heart I talk to about
the convergence of guilt and denial
flowing together toward
the ocean of self. But it doesn't listen
because I pollute it every day.
Someday my heart may
be made of plastic, but I fear it is already.
Too many words I say but don't mean
tangle in the branches of my silence.
It's like I want to be liked
but I don't want to be liked.
It's like the silence too though
suffocates me, catches in my throat.
The wind it drags through me makes me
not hear others when they speak.
When the silence quiets itself enough
even the moon speaks louder from the dark
than the moon spooning the edges
of poems streaming inside me. Even the rest
of the trees flower like songs.
I hear so many voices, I think I hear voices.
Voices other than my own I hope
I'll carry with me moving forward.
I won't speak until they ask me to

but when they ask me to, I won't speak.
I won't rattle on as usual. I'll come down —
calm down. I'll open like a cloud, so slowly
no one will see it happening.

Iain Twiddy
MONORAIL

Looking down,
standing-swaying,
Ōsaka monorail spacily
over the motorways, flyways,
blankly stilting the city,

curving lunarly in
to the chore of the airport,
the twenty-air-hours-ahead,
nearly-day-behind
conference, where

I will connect with no-one;
looking down, yawning,
late autumn late morning,
head as empty
as the sky of clouds,

to a parking attendant
just then resplendent in blue,
standing around,
batoned and capped,
looking yawning up.

Bruce Robinson
UPTOWN

The sure extinction that we travel to...

Once past Chambers you're almost there, fourteenth
twenty-third, thirty-fourth Penn, only as long
as we can stand our ground. No more

than the tunnel of Penn, you know, its fetid
air, rebuke on a wall, and simpler
to mourn than the stops you used to call

your family. Is that the way each ticket rides,
its adult fare, the slowdown on the tracks
a pediment, what thou lov'st well

is less than clear, a flicker, then a right of way,
a lantern then a windowpane, a loop
of film that spins too fast to care,

an uptown stop you pass right by, your mind
in some rearranged way occupied,
under the world or above it all,

the window closing, the open air?
Was I once lost? The route's not clear but
those must be my hands on that wall.

Anthony Warnke
YOU WANT TO EAT YOUR JOB

You want to eat your job
in one large, painful meal.
You want to eat your job
like this warm, French bread. No,
with this warm French bread, for digestion.

You want to throw up from the pressure.
Your commute is long. You start out
from empty space. Office conga lines
are not compulsory, but everyone
joins in, including you. "Come on,
Jason!" and your name's not Jason.
You just received your 15-year pin,

and it says *Congratulations, Jason.* You
think you want to quit, and politely,
ask for the opposite.

You don't know any better.

Ana Caballero
MARCH

It was their quietness that made me lean toward them fascinated
the first time I saw the axolotls. --Julio Cortázar

Leticia and Jerry decided to co-quarantine on the morning of their
fifth consecutive night in bed together, some two weeks after that
glacial early morning, silent and ashen as an oyster that failed to
open, when Jerry stopped to fix the sudden gash on Leticia's front
bike tire on the Columbia Street Waterfront Greenway. Leticia
watched as this thin, agile stranger—who'd jumped off his own bike
without a sound, his face shielded against the piercing cold by a
black ski mask—pulled out tools and patches from a nylon sack, his
gloved fingers familiar, comfortable, with the work at hand. *There's a
deli on Hicks and Kane,* Jerry had said. *Congress is just a couple of blocks
down. We can take it to cross the BQE. I recommend riding there. I can follow
you. So we can make sure the patch worked. You could really freeze out here
on a morning like this.* The patch held, and at the deli, Leticia bought
coffee. When Jerry shed his ski mask, two brown spoon-shaped eyes
emerged. Their steady gaze reminded Leticia of a shelf stocked with
provisions.

Two weeks later, there they lay—sipping coffee, naked from the
waist down, propped up on pillows, scrolling through articles on
their silvery laptops. The State's email, reminding all citizens of the
impending start of that year's Annual Quarantine Month, pinged
both their inboxes simultaneously. It had been over seven years since
the initial virus outbreaks devastated the State, which had been
quick to determine that compulsory, annual quarantines were the
only effective weapon to prevent waves of deadlier viral strains from
emerging. The only way to keep the populace safe, the State insisted,
was by keeping people inside their homes for one month every year,
regardless of the mounting effectivity of vaccination campaigns.
Whatever was inevitably brewing amongst the population at large,
the State decreed, would diminish by keeping random bodies apart.

Have you registered for Quarantine Month? Jerry asked. Leticia shook
her head, *No.*

We could quarantine together, Jerry said, his eagerness curbed by the risk of rejection. *Yes,* she responded simply, *yes*.

The tips of their fingers logged onto the State's Quarantine Registrar, where each individual was required by law to declare the name of the persons, if any, with whom they would spend the thirty-one days of March, now known as Quarantine Month. Simultaneously, they typed in each other's name.

That first March they spent together in absolute isolation in Jerry's brownstone basement apartment, located on the block right before Carrol Gardens becomes Red Hook, was nothing short of grotesque, Leticia would later relate to her roommates. Grotesque in a great way. Not only was it love at, basically, first sight, she confirmed, but it was artistically scorching.

The manufacture of clothing is so violent, Leticia explained to Jerry one night, a week or so into their month-long mandatory confinement, the overripe color of her eyes fogged by the pitch dark of his basement apartment where light from the outside world had trouble entering. *Nothing is as vicious as an industrial sewing machine. The way clothes are produced is a mad stabbing of fabric, fabric we slip onto our bodies. At first, I thought that by stapling clothing to canvases I could show this violence. Maybe I was naïve to want this, but I did. I wanted people to see, then feel, the hidden hostility in the mass production of soft, even delicate, objects. But then, the virus came, and everything changed. Nothing was as savage as the virus. As how the virus enters our bodies. Slowly shutting us down. Choking us. From within. I stopped stapling clothes. I started piercing the canvas with thread. When I do it, I feel I am the virus piercing people's skin, their bodies. Their organs. But, when I draw the needle out, it's also me, only this time I am sucking the virus out.*

Doesn't it depress you, to relive the virus like that, every day, when you work?

Yes. It does.

They were silent after that. Then Jerry reached over and held her. And, though they were both of slight build, his grip over her was conclusive, his hold. So, too, his hardening. That night, their bodies thrust together as if attempting to reach, to scrub clean, each other's secret pockets of muck. Leticia had had a few boyfriends before, but she never considered labeling any of it as love because she never felt like the part of her that actually contained her had ever been penetrated. As a result, she had come to believe that there simply was no such thing as touch.

After her month interment with Jerry, her work's focus, which had suffered a serrated rebirth after her mother's death eight years prior during the virus' nightmarish Second Wave, became less about incursion and more about incorporation—about absorption. Never had Leticia produced such essential work, puncturing the dozen medium-sized canvases she'd brought with her to Jerry's place with vermilion, ochre, magenta, bergamot-colored threads, trapping every sliver of canvas with her fury of woven texture. *Just look at the work I am producing; we are so in love*, Leticia proclaimed, meaning it.

Moving in with Jerry after the end of their first Quarantine Month together was a nominal process. She'd already brought most of her significant belongings with her for their four weeks of sheltering in place, not that she had much by way of stuff. When she met Jerry, she'd been living in Red Hook for a little over two years, in an airy if dingy fourth-story walk-up that she shared with two friends who had graduated with her from Savannah's School of Art and Design. The three of them amassed their dorm room furniture into the frank geometry of the two-bedroom apartment, switching bedrooms in four-month intervals so that each had the chance to sleep in the south-facing bedroom, whose side views of the Verrazano Narrows Bridge suffused onlookers with a narrative of possibility. Such arrangement also meant that each girl spent four months of the year sleeping on a futon in the living room. Leticia's futon *terzo* occurred during Quarantine Month each year, a cycle she requested, a cycle her roommates readily granted.

From spending five consecutive Quarantine Months with her father in his small Fort Lauderdale condo (she'd drive down from Savannah to be with him as soon as classes paused in preparation for the month of remote learning), Leticia had realized that people tended to limit themselves to their bedrooms during enforced isolation, leaving the rest of the living space virtually uninhabited. It was during this time that she picked up cooking and cleaning in earnest, activities she could only savor if performed under rigorous solitude. Before her father woke, she was up disinfecting surfaces, dishing breakfast, and preparing the single elaborate meal of the day—lunch. After lunch she worked and studied in the living room, while her father read in his bedroom until dinner, which her father was charged with preparing. He never managed to present more than a platter of Leticia's irregularly warmed leftovers—but she didn't mind. Like this, they dwelled within a routine of contained, hushed tending and their month together, with its otherwise confrontational absence of mother, felt like something more than mere survival.

The same happened in Red Hook—Leticia's roommates hardly entered the kitchen before noon, leaving her to clean and prepare whatever meals she wished in peace. Before the first of March, they each contributed a portion of their paltry, entry-level salaries to the pantry fund. Somehow, Leticia managed to deliver elaborate meals each day—herb-roasted chicken, goulash, curried garbanzos, cinnamon-fried plantains, quinoa-stuffed peppers, lathered tahini, and pastas in every iteration imaginable. Since none of the girls could afford to pay the high pre-Quarantine Month ticket prices to fly to their families, Leticia's cossetting grounded them in a way that felt like home.

When she told her roommates she was quarantining with Jerry, the Jerry she had met just two weeks ago, they were not as concerned by the swiftness of her decision as by its timing.

What if you get sick of each other halfway through? Who's going to cook for us? Does he have a living room? Where will you work? Can you prepare and freeze dishes for us? Are you sure he's not a freak? Leticia left them unanswered.

Her father's questions, though, she addressed.

Leticia, how is he?

He is hardworking, Dad. He lost his older sister to the virus; she had diabetes. His grandparents, too, of course.

Leticia — Leti, are you sure?

Yes, she pressed, *yes*. Then, cautiously, but aware her father would not know how to respond, she ended the conversation, *he is like us*.

She kept quiet until he seemed to soften, until he sighed, and less assertively muttered, *Okay, Leti, okay.*

Leticia had in fact meant exactly what she said. To her, *like us* was a transparent phrase, with no generational, no father/daughter decryption required. *Like us* meant like us. Not just hurt — like us — but evidently maimed. In Leticia's mind, she and her father belonged not to the ranks of the wounded, but to the very substance of wound. Leticia's father, a straightforward, well-liked high school history teacher, had married once and late in life to the woman he joked was his hot trophy wife, Leticia's mother, a proficient nurse at Fort Lauderdale's Holy Cross Hospital. They had lived in a small but relatively new condo with a small pool and a small Intracoastal view. They had wanted nothing more.

Now, eight years and eight Quarantine Months after her mother's death, Leticia was surprised to feel so, so — unprepared. *I should be better at this*, she thought, sitting in Jerry's kitchen, her kitchen for the past year, surrounded by the stack of blank canvases she'd lugged all the way from Michael's earlier that day in preparation for tomorrow's lockdown under a sky so opaque it could only mean snow. She counted. Five Quarantine Months with her father. Two with her Red Hook roommates. Then, that grotesquely epic one with Jerry last year. *It's been fine before, hasn't it?*

She was sure it wasn't fear of the virus's taking, of its abrupt carnage, that unsettled her — no, the fear was over. Despite alarming bursts of infectious mutations, vaccines had the virus itself under control. Many even questioned the continued need for Quarantine Month. Even so, the economy had adapted to eleven months of pedestrian commerce and one month of quarantine-based business during which the State hired millions of workers to hand-stitch next-generation facemasks.

This is how Leticia discovered sewing. That first Quarantine Month after her mother's death, she registered to receive a case of facemasks at her father's Fort Lauderdale condo. These masks required hand stitching to snugly fit the ten different State-designated face sizes. "One size fits all" masks allowed the virus access to certain face shapes' open cavities. Once this issue was identified, the State conducted a digital face census, requiring all citizens to send in a close-up selfie. The nation's jaws, cheek bones, nose widths, chin dips, lip curves and face widths were mapped into ten categories, each assigned a tailored mask shape that fit each the wearer's face in a private, deliberate way.

It took Leticia two weeks to sew her case of facemasks, working into the night as if keeping vigil. Once she was done, she kept sewing — she took the clothing she had planned to staple and cobbled it onto her canvases, using the leftovers from the State's facemask sewing kit.

I should be looking forward to this, Leticia thought. *Another Quarantine Month with Jerry.* The thin wooden pantry was stocked. The cleaning supply cabinet, too. Now she'd brought her art materials home. Home. Was this place home? So far, it was a life, an adult life. Besides Leticia's solemn cooking and their sporadic yet frenetic love making, there were plenty of other activities they shared, other pursuits by which they amassed their days into months: endless bike rides, books and culture magazines, probing walks, museum exhibits, and the seasonal tilling of the backyard shared by the residents of the brownstone apartment complex. Jerry's intermediate position at an established Manhattan ad agency afforded them the income to eat out with their fistful of friends. Her own job at a fledgling gallery paid little but opened doors for her art, plus they let her use a small corner of their storage area to work on her own pieces. None of it was bad.

She even had a solution to the recent slump in her work—that visceral satisfaction she derived from the willful perforation of linen by thread, the crafted tumult that lent her canvases the quality of beautiful bruised pulp, was fading. The energy that meeting Jerry had injected into her life, too, was spent. Even her work had begun to feel like work and its constancy like another element within her increasingly stabilized, settled existence. *I need to cut the fat, the excess meat,* she realized, mulling over a near-finished piece at her gallery's warehouse. She took a set of scissors from the packaging room and sliced into the stretched linen, into her embroidery, fraying weeks of painstaking work. The next morning, she added X-ACTO knives to her Michael's lockdown shopping list, the X-ACTO knives she'd tossed onto Jerry's small round kitchen table, her small kitchen table, where they had landed with the grace of a metallic octopus.

Leticia picked up one of the knives, still frigid from the outside cold, and began peeling its tight plastic wrap. She wished she had entered her father's name into the State's Quarantine Registrar, even if that meant scrambling to find a way to fly south to Fort Lauderdale, even if that meant sharing the apartment with his new live-in girlfriend, whose figure had grazed the frame of Leticia's screen during a recent Saturday morning Facetime chat.

Dad, was that Badia? Leticia had asked, trying to keep her tone flat.

Yes. She moved in, Leti.

For a moment, neither spoke—they were as quiet as a cotton ball being pulled apart.

I didn't know it had gotten so serious, Leticia said, finally. She knew her father had begun seeing their Moroccan downstairs neighbor toward her final months at Savannah, but she had assumed—hoped—it would remain casual. This, however, was not a thought she was able to admit to herself, or to anyone else. Seeing her father move on from her mother's death reinforced the idea that she had also moved on, that both of them had rebuilt their lives and were doing fine. But she had not rebuilt herself. Somewhere, inside, she was only going through the motions of her honeyed, established life.

Somewhere, deep inside, even beyond Jerry's intentional reach, she was permanently, irretrievably crushed.

Things evolved over the past year. It just made sense for her to move in. Especially now that you're settled with Jerry.

What does my living with Jerry have to do with it?

Her father took an audible breath and paused, then said, —precise as precipice—*lockdown alone is hard.*

Leticia wished she could've answered, *lockdown with anyone* is hard. But she didn't. She couldn't permit entry to the reality that, even with Jerry, the days of Quarantine Month, the days of all months, were hard. Too much silence passed, and a sliding door shut between them. They returned to their world of courtesy, of discretion, of restrained communal hurt.

It's good you are settled, Dad.

Yes, Leti. It's good we both are.

Yes.

Badia has a tagine recipe she wants me to send you.

Send it over. I still have a few days to scrounge for supplies.

Leticia did not tell Jerry about Badia, did not buy the ingredients for Badia's tagine. And now, tomorrow, or rather that night at one in the morning, lockdown began, and people would only be allowed to walk the streets singly, quiet as concrete, like a silent film record of present time. To the grocery, the pharmacy, the laundry—and back. Her breath entered her chest as gasps. It was too late now, to go anywhere, fly anywhere, too late—and against Quarantine Law. On an impulse, she called her father, a ritual she observed only on Saturday mornings.

Leti, congrats, her father exclaimed in greeting. *I am so happy for you and Jerry. I couldn't ask for a better son-in-law.*

What? Leti whispered. *What? Dad, what are you talking about?*

Oh, God. Shit. Don't tell me Jerry hasn't proposed yet. Damn it. Leti, I am so sorry. He told me he was proposing tonight, on the eve of Quarantine Month. I thought you were calling to share the news. He asked for your hand last week.

He's not here yet, she responded meekly. *I, I was just calling to make sure you were all set for lockdown.*

Yes Leti, Badia and I are fine. Oh God. Promise me you'll act surprised when he asks. Okay? Please.

I promise.

Call us tomorrow so we can congratulate you, Sweetie. Okay? We're so happy for you.

Okay.

I have to run. Badia and I were about to go on a last walk before they cage us in. Bye, Leti.

Bye, Dad.

Leticia stared at the table, her table. Any minute Jerry would walk in and find her there— X-ACTO knives, thread, canvases strewn across compact space. She got up and started collecting her things, her mess. It would be tight, but if she hurried, she'd have just enough time to wipe the kitchen clean.

John Niebuhr
WE WILL ALL SUBSCRIBE AGAIN

Soon we must unplug
everything.

All clocks will freeze
mid-mantra

and we will hang fruit
to tell the time.

–

Our lights have been flickering,
their voices

stuttering mid-song.
We worry

this will continue.
Sometimes it does.

–

There are too many songs
playing at once

to enjoy any particular one.
Even fruit flies

change their minds and dive
mid-flight into the vinegar.

–

Once all lights synchronize
in their turning off

earth will fade mid-orbit,
absent from time,

and we will all
subscribe again.

Amanda Ganus
NOTES FROM THE INSIDE

Most days, I view my body from the inside. I feel pain in my heel and see the plantar fascia tendon peeling from bone as it has been doing continually since college. This was back when I was merely "overweight," still playing with the boundary of socially acceptable size. This was before I was "obese," which is a risk factor for this bone and tendon separation. My plantar fascia must have known what was coming and decided to get a head start.

In January, when I had a tumor removed from my breast, I saw the hole it created from the inside, beyond the sutures. I watched as flesh came together to fill the void. My partner watched the outside where the jagged wound around my areola slowly stitched itself back together to form a jagged line of flesh. He ran his finger along the line gently, as if he loved this new, changing part of me. When I asked him about it, he leaned down and kissed it, then my lips, then my forehead. He did not ask what it looked like inside. He did not know I could see it.

When my lungs do not work because I have weathered too much bronchitis and too many allergies, I see them as they struggle to expand. I travel down my throat with the puff of albuterol into my lungs, watching the sacs gain life again. I see the air moving through as I take deep breaths, catching up on the oxygen I had been denied.

I see the cysts on my ovaries pulsing, feel their sharp pain. They tell me I am fertile, or maybe that I'm not, but I should keep taking my birth control to keep the pain at bay.

I see a kidney stone forming and knocking against the organ wall, urging me to drink more water and break down its calcified edges. It reminds me of the last time, the crying, the vomiting, the morphine. I can watch it, but I cannot touch it, which means I cannot fix it myself.

I am a spectator to my sinus cavities, which are filling with fluid because I walked through a park after forgetting to take my allergy medication. As I ignore the needs of my sinuses, I am helping to push the cavities beyond their natural boundaries, pressuring them and causing the headache. When I take the medication meant to help the pain, I stop pushing and watch the cavities empty again until the medicine wears off and I have to help push again.

I wish I could see my brain. I would watch the synapses firing for ages, pinging to one another all the information they need to keep me alive, keep me thinking, keep me human. I would sit in a groove of my grey matter, watching for any synapses that did not make it to their destination in the amygdala, that got lost or fired at the wrong time, leading to a synaptic traffic jam. I would see the traffic jam just as my lungs began to constrict again, my hands began to shake, and my eyes turned to my partner in desperation, signaling to him the start of another panic attack. Just before the first panicked tear fell, I would stop my lungs, my hands, my eyes. I would tell my partner I was fine, it was only a lost synapse, and I would go back to watching.

Devon Balwit
MISTAKEN

He felt for his food.
His fingers had the noses of weasels.
I couldn't stop looking.
                    --Plath, "Little Fugue"

How is it then, the very mornings I feel best,
I flense myself in search of incipient sickness, lest

I have nothing to lament. Surely something wobbles,
set to veer off course. Though silent, some trouble

slouches out of sight. Like a weasel in a wall,
I hunt blind pinkies, alert to the rise and fall

of the newest newborn chest. I skip past
feel-good stories in the paper, seeking the direst

headlines, comparing and stockpiling. Which ones
have it worse? These have gnawed suffering to the bone,

then boiled the bone and drunk the broth again.
Like the pus from cowpox, I want inoculation,

a way to minimize infection once it comes.
Like one boarding over windows before the drum

of hurricane winds, I call my premature darkness
prescience, mistaking dread for readiness.

Andrew Ban
TIME TRAVEL

Scrolling through Twitter
I saw my friend make a joke.

I thought nothing of it
and scrolled down.

Ten minutes later I saw it again.
It said hashtag funny,
the same one as last time.

I went down and told my mom,
I think I time-traveled.

She said it was a retweet.
She told me I was so naive.

Lauren Claus
LAB RESULT

The day of my diagnosis, I wanted
   woods— silt over stone, fallen brush.

Nothing is clean. Here, nothing is afraid
   to touch me. No nurse at the door

with a smile. No doctor, gloves
   over hands. Only the leaves are left.

The soil. The shit of the starling. It's natural
   enough to be remnant. We all think

the body will not break,
   until it does. Dross of heartwood,

primrose leaf.

Holly Eva Allen
BROCA'S APHASIA

The mind's great faculties worn,
some slick of once-sturdy cerebellum washes away
in a steady stream of rain water,
down it goes,
down the drain.

Capitulating to God's fierce fancies,
he offers up his kind language.
Goodbye to his goodbyes,
his easy greetings too,
all verbiage vanished.

These difficulties will remain unnamed,
for their names are too plosive, too severe.
The easy slurs come first.
We learn with him,
this new language.

This misarticulate mumbling,
this ballad of honeybees and wind.
We learn to hear what he is saying
as he learns to say it.

Brett Thompson
GRIEF

We set out upon the ice
scuffing off the layers of snow
with the soles of our boots
to look down at the lake bed
where her face would be
for one last moment,
returning our gaze
like the fractured reflection
in a windswept puddle.
This is the truth:
It was November
and we gathered
by the edge of open water
and shivered in the sudden cold.
You puffed on a stale Winston
that you claimed was in her honor
but we all knew
it was all bullshit, especially
when you stamped it out
and walked the mile home
on your two good legs
which were strong and white
and always moving forward.

Avery K. James
TO THE BLACK BOY: ALMOST

You were so close to home when they shot you.
The streetlights leaned low to warm your pumice
face, gazed, and knew you were not some loveless,
strange danger even when the men in blue
said you were. You tried to speak and out flew
a confused animal of sound, sunless
song, pulses of aimless blood. Oh, luckless
boy. I saw them darken an avenue
with you, saw you just as the streetlights did—
too small for your clothes, too small for decay.
When the newsmen come, I'll tell them you sung.
They'll tell me: that sound can't come from a kid.
I'll tuck my rage, tell them I heard you say,
I didn't do it. Still, the bullet stung.

Brian Gatz
FREAK WEATHER

Next up for me is next up.
     Loss colors all I've got
with what I haven't got.
     Rumors of snow
last day of June.
Only happens once?
     Only happiness of
not happening at all.
     What was before
now isn't. What was before
- even memories - isn't now.

That's winter June
     from January carried
past February, sacrificed,
     through March battled
into April's lengthening May,
     and so on,
opened to a snowstorm
     so far south
in summer's number one month.
     All's assumed the change,
     all's freighted with come-what-may,
     all that and nothing comes again.

Cait West
GOING DUTCH

"Dykema," he grumbles while placing a call-in order for two loaves of raisin bread, no cinnamon. I've seen him in the bakery before and recognize his voice: a disgruntled old man whose volume is always turned up.

"Can you spell that, please?" I ask politely, pen in hand.

"It's a common name!" Dykema. A common name — in one county in one state in America. D-y-k-e-m-a. Even though my husband has the longest Dutch surname I've ever seen, I'm new to this area, and I still have to practice my Dutch spelling.

I hang up the phone and set aside two sliced raisin loaves, the sugar sticking to the plastic bags. I know it won't be long before Mr. Dykema marches in, demanding his bread after shrieking "Konnichi wa" at me. Every day, it's the same. He was in World War II, which means he learned two Japanese words and wants everyone else to know it. I don't like to be yelled at, so I've learned to avoid eye contact, count his change quickly, and not respond to his prodding. But I've also learned that I can give him day-old bread and he won't know the difference.

The Dutch community in West Michigan has managed to squeeze a nation-sized ego into three or four small towns huddled next to the lakeshore. Being blunt is a virtue here. My husband's Netherlander grandfather says, "If you ain't Dutch, you ain't much." I reply, "But I'm not Dutch, Opa," only to be rebuked with: "Well, you are now!"

Having no previous job experience at the age of twenty-five, I somehow managed to get hired at this little hole-in-the-wall Dutch bakery down the street from my first apartment. I have an inkling that this only happened because my desperate resume included the job description "church pianist," implying a respectable upbringing. Like many of the Dutch descendants in West Michigan, the bakery owner is Christian Reformed, which means the shop is closed Sundays and employee tasks are strictly gender-segregated.

As one of the Ladies, my job of menial labor begins at five or six in the morning. As I walk from the still-dark parking lot through the back door, a wave of heat from the walk-in oven hits my face. It smells like burnt sugar and hot grease. I get to work immediately: boxing donuts, slicing bread, and placating irritable customers who wanted printed and not cursive writing on their cakes. Soon, smeared chocolate and purple icing stain my crisp white apron. It already feels like a long day. While the line of customers grows and the sun lights up the street, the Bakers (note, they are not called the Gentlemen or even the Men) are pulling the last donuts from the hot fryer and wiping down the giant wooden table in the back. They stack person-sized bags of flour and tubs of cherry filling, each weighing about fifty pounds. The Bakers' night shift is almost over, and they will go home for a few hours' sleep before coming back to proof dough and grease cake pans. Later, when school lets out in the afternoon, the Girls will come in to take over the counter and wash the iron trays sticky with frosting.

I grow to hate this job, but I love work and what it means: a paycheck written to my name and the freedom to spend it on anything from piercings to tattoos to rock concerts. Truth be told, I am ten years behind most people my age. While my peers were going to college and building job experience, I was kept home after high school to learn homemaking skills and prepare to be a stay-at-home wife and mother. I'm now in my mid-twenties, married without my father's approval, and working my first minimum-wage job after running away from my restricted life. If anyone should run wild, it's me. But I already feel too old for the fun of anything that my parents would have deemed rebellious. So instead of splurging with my hard-earned money, I end up paying rent and budgeting for groceries. Still, I drive the grocery cart through the aisles like I own them. More importantly, this desire for ownership drives me, a desire to own myself and my life, a desire to fight back and fight forward.

The bakery's strict gender roles are not unfamiliar to me: the women wearing aprons and providing a pretty face to the public while the men do the heavy lifting. I know how the system works. It's not a joke when I say I grew up in a family that was proudly part of the Christian patriarchy movement, which is exactly what it sounds like. I was taught that limitations on women were a good thing, that they were a protection. That being given no choice in my future would ensure protection from heartbreak, from failure. Except I never felt protected, just trapped.

In this fringe group of fundamentalism, I was one of many so-called stay-at-home daughters. We were predestined to be wives and mothers only: any other kind of work or education was forbidden. Speaking up was unthinkable, punishable, rebellious. When I try to explain my past to a coworker, she ends up classifying me as formerly Amish. I almost correct her, but then, what's the point? We weren't Pennsylvania Dutch, but we did live in the country, where we occasionally wore denim jumpers and were taught about courtship, patriarchy, and how to hate yourself if you're a woman.

My older sister Mandie avoided denim, but she was the real baker of the family. Mandie knew how to braid and bake dough into beautiful loaves of bread, brushing egg yolk over the tops to make them golden. She could tier cakes and pipe intricate basket weaves with frosting. She could make stunning pecan pies and chocolate-chip banana muffins. She made food gorgeous, but sometimes the cakes were dry on the inside.

Mandie's first job was at a Dutch bakery, too, at the base of the mountain in Colorado where we lived, when she was about twenty and I was eleven. I remember her leaving for the whole day and coming home exhausted but happy. I visited her once during the brief time she was allowed to work there. It was a small, quiet storefront with a greenish murky light leaking in the windows. Clean aluminum counters gleamed in the back. She showed me how she frosted cakes on a spinning plate. She had a job, and she was good at it. But this exception to our household rule of women not working didn't last long.

Later, my father would say it was a mistake, letting her work there, letting her have a job. Of course, it wasn't a mistake until she nearly eloped with one of her coworkers. I remember driving home from church the Sunday she stayed behind with the quiet man who had slipped into the service late. I thought I'd never see her again. I didn't understand what was happening except that she was getting married in a couple hours, and my parents had left church without her. My father was driving us up the mountain in one of his silent rages, my mother weeping uncontrollably in the passenger seat. She kept saying, "She always wanted a big wedding. She gets *Bride* magazine!" Even on "normal" days there was always an underlying tension between my parents as they sat facing the same direction in the car or as they worked in their separate areas at home: my mother often in the kitchen, my father in his office in the basement. But on this day, I remember thinking it was like my sister had died.

It didn't take long for my sister to change her mind. After I had very seriously written her eulogy in my diary, the phone rang, and she wanted to come home.

After that, Mandie didn't work anymore. She was repentant, quieter, sewing quilts all day in a one-window closet she called the Sewing Room. Forgiven and compliant. I have always wondered if those few hours when she was left behind felt like freedom to her, or too much like the oppression of choice when you've never had any. Or maybe the threat of never seeing her family again was too much for her conscience. I know the feeling.

This small-town Michigan bakery is my first job after leaving a world I never felt completely a part of. Unlike my sister, I ran away before getting a job. But I won't stay here for more than a couple years. I will grow tired of the early mornings, the nine-hour shifts with no breaks, the customers with their sugar anxieties. I will want more than eleven-cent tips in a jar we're not allowed to label "Tips." I will be insulted by the sign on the ancient freezer in the back which says, "No Ladies Allowed," implying we are not strong enough to close tight the broken door. But for all its faults, this job is still better than my previous life: I can quit when I want to, and no one is making me spend my time in a closet.

My grandmom, who was from Yonkers (once known as New Amsterdam) and whose last job was at a bakery called Dunkin' Donuts, once wrote me the following advice: "Dear, I am going to talk to you like a Dutch uncle. You should not be so hard on yourself, you always do your best." I'm not sure she understood the true implications of having Dutch relatives, but her words stuck with me. For so long, I lived in a harsh world—a world where, to survive, I needed to submit without question—and I rarely felt like a good person, much less someone capable of "doing my best." But somehow her belief in me made a difference. It helped keep alive the spark of wanting to be myself, to be capable of having a "best." It took me a long time to find the strength to leave and find my own way in life, and I might not have more to show for it than a dingy second-floor apartment, a manual labor job, my best friend who is now my husband, and secondhand copies of the *Harry Potter* series I'm now allowed to read. But I have my freedom. I have much to learn about life and about myself. For now, what matters most to me is that I get to decide who I am from here.

Risa Pappas
SOMETHING IS DIFFERENT

They must be velveting, becoming antlers.
I rub my ears down on trees,
sharpen myself against bark and stone.
Or my ears go long like a rabbit's
to hear sharp sounds from far depths
that spread from the sides of my face
and curl my lips into a snagtooth snarl.
Nose become snout. I smell the change
in me, guts realigning. As a child
to stop my breasts from budding
I screamed until my nose bled.
My discomfort is now comforting.
Finally, a commandment from my mind
carried out by the body.
I walk hand in talon with it
into whatever I am becoming.

Marcus Whalbring
EASTER SUNDAY

Then my son held a slug on the back of his hand
way longer than I think most people would.
A strand of its slime stretched from his thumb
to his forefinger. A string of lubricant some
would wretch at if they felt it stitched
between digits like someone else's spit. But he let it
sit between his knuckles as he pressed
gently on its back and made a fist
he raised to my face, letting me see
like he was doing better than me on a test
and this was one of the answers.
Don't you want to hunt for eggs? I asked. No,
not yet. By late afternoon, it had found his wrist
and rested on the warmth of his pulse
that flickered like a flame of fresh petal under his flesh.
It read the brevity of his life there until dinner
when he gave it back to the garden.
Before bed that night, he wondered aloud
if the slug would follow him forever, now
that it knew his heart like the rhythm of the soil
or the warmth of a sidewalk wet after a late rain.
He hoped it would bend toward him always,
I think, and he'd never be alone again.
I let him believe it.
People have believed stranger things
for centuries. Some of them were okay.
And what if he's right? What if
we each have a slug sliding down the pavement
trying to catch us, knowing it never will,
drawing a line of slime we could follow
back to who we once were when
there was more wonder than uncertainty,
when the world seemed ready to hatch before us
and even the backs of our hands were a mystery?

Risa Pappas
I PRESUPPOSED THIS SOMEONE
TO BE A MAN

My nails were painted
the spectrum a peach
lives; I splayed my fingers out
the way you do when you play stickum
on the wood. The sun had gone
to bed suddenly
and soon it was dark.

I looked at my hands.
Rings had grown over each finger, fused
to the tabletop so I couldn't lift them.
I'd waited all that time
for the opportunity to escape
to pass me by.

To my left, a pitcher of sun
tea sat, ice cubes
swirling and clinking like music
against the crying glass.

Marcus Whalbring
IN THE KITCHEN AT NIGHT

He should've been in bed. But he was there
at the table, full of sleep, asking me
how not to think about dying. So
we talked about the soul and where it goes
once it takes the body off, and we agreed
there must be a room
and maybe the room is full of doughnuts and comic books,
maybe it's full of grass and there's room to do
whatever the soul's version of running is,
maybe the room is the kind of room that can be a room
without walls, maybe there's no need for doctors there,
maybe doctors turn into pillows,
but maybe we won't need pillows, maybe
no one can see you
except the trees, but maybe the trees think everyone looks funny
so it doesn't matter if they think you do too.
And maybe no one knows what dying feels like
so maybe it feels like taking a bite
of something you've never tasted before that's not so bad,
or maybe it's like learning a word in a new language,
which is like teaching your mouth to tie its shoes,
which is something he hadn't learned to do yet,
which I reminded him was okay, and he reminded me
we were talking about dying and what it was like
and I reminded him
there are people who go to sleep and don't wake up,
which most agree is probably the best way to go, and he
wondered if that was true, and I said it was, and I said
maybe dying is like when you have to fart really bad
and maybe dying sounds like farting
and every time you hear a fart, a ghost is crossing over,
and I made a fart noise with my mouth,
which made him laugh, and after he laughed I asked
if he was okay now, and he said he was,
and I walked him to his room

and helped him climb
to the top bunk and brought the sheet to his chin
and he said goodnight after I said it, and I went
to bed after he did, and I hoped we'd both dream
of something good or nothing at all,
which is the same thing
and I dreamt of nothing at all,
and I forgot to ask him what he dreamt
and he forgot to tell me, and we both forgot
to turn off the kitchen light before bed so I turned it off
that morning because the sun was up,
and we didn't need it on anymore.

Martin Arnold
PLAYBOY

My nine-year-old stumbles descending
the final stair, hemispheres
encompassing each ear. How are you?
generates an Off-Air expression.
Outside, the sun slides in chutes.
Months inside a Covid-19 bubble,
my son's hair flies to one side,
a wave parted by a monolith.
He dons underwear, possibly clean,
beneath a fuzzy crimson bathrobe
like a young Hugh Hefner.

He's come down for a snack.
He hasn't worn clothes in weeks.

He could be an advertisement:
Don't let this happen to you!
  or the vision that sent Thoreau
stumbling toward Flint's Pond.

He could be a mad scientist
massaging the brain of a robot
with six ears, a screen
displaying its thoughts, a mind
of infinite connectivity.
He's built to be better than we are:
the future in search of a body
to bear it clumsily through the world.

Lauren Claus
DESPITE LUPUS

As if snow could sift itself,
  he left her
the bare and bright expanse. The fissured door.
   As if her body
     did not break.
   Nights, each rend of ice —
[v]. a tear and then *a rupture.*
  Ridge and rafter,
angle turning straight,
she knew the last time he heard her
  and listened.
  The broken gate,
  and beyond roots loosened by runoff.
It is quiet,
  sinking.
Then slipping back into light.

Heather Quinn
SONG

CAST
POET – Writes in Neighborhood Park under cypress tree called "Tree."
(to be played by Scuffed Black Shoe & Starling)

MOTHER – Elderly mother of Poet in hospital despite Poet giving
her his last mask at beginning of outbreak.
(to be played by Paper Lantern Tossed by Ocean)

OFFICER – Walks Neighborhood Park beat. Notebook entry at
start of shift: "Hot day. Seek shade."
(to be played by Waterless Tea Kettle)

NURSE – Works at Hospital. Senses an invisible root running from
her navel to Mother's navel; has never felt this kind of connection
before & thought it was indigestion until realizing her belly is
humming at the vibration of music
(to be played by Plump Apple)

STRAY – Neighborhood Park regular
(to be played by Dog)

SCENE I
Poet sits & writes under Tree, "I have lost my words"
Wind blows Poet's words from page through Neighborhood Park
Words swirl like leaves then:

"I" thumps Stray's left ear (Stray lets loose loud howl)

"words" hangs by its "s" on Tree

"have" & "my" float to sky

"lost" flies into Officer's eyes

Officer swats "lost" away & spots Poet sitting in public without mask
Officer demands explanation
Poet tries to speak but cannot
Draws picture instead

Officer (turning burnt red) rips picture in two
Confiscates journal
Hands Poet citation for subversive activity
Points & shouts: *Lock him up!*

SCENE II
Poet transforms into Starling, flies through cell bars into night sky
& perches on windowsill of Mother's hospital room

Poet knocks on window with beak

Nurse opens window, nods in recognition, lets Poet in & places
paper cup full of Mother's tears before Poet

Nurse leaves room as Poet drinks from cup then perches on
Mother's shoulder

Mother's tears illuminate Poet's beak & when Poet starts to sing
fireflies rush from mouth

Mother gasps in delight

SCENE III
Poet eats lyrics from songbook left by Nurse on Mother's bedside
table

Poet (singing to Mother):
Night is a warm blanket to rock you to sleep
To carry you to dreams so sweet

Mother tries to sing along but coughs uncontrollably

Nurse hurries into room then calls Code Ventilator

Poet flaps wings in fright as fireflies light up Mother's chest

[Fireflies flicker & fade out]

Suphil Lee Park
FORWARD

Be more than the crocuses
           that shiver like champagne
glasses that you're carrying on a tray
           of your mind into my future.
Every street, a whirlwind
           of flower shops. Take this
Swiss knife and slash the stomach
           of a river open, and you'll find
some light there. Spruce up every corner
           with a bird bath, we'll find more
light there. Even when I thwart
my thirst and quench my qualms
by accident —
           such happenstance
           light is goaded by.
I'll fist in my fist yards of red silk
and pretend it to be my heart.
I'll punch you, I'll punch you
twice.

Hannah Marshall
ACHSAH CONSIDERS WRITING
TO HER FATHER

> *And Caleb said, He that smiteth Kirjathsepher, and taketh*
> *it, to him will I give Achsah my daughter to wife. And*
> *Othniel the son of Kenaz, Caleb's younger brother, took it:*
> *and he gave him Achsah his daughter to wife.*
> ...
> *And she said unto him, Give me a blessing: for thou hast*
> *given me a south land; give me also springs of water. And*
> *Caleb gave her the upper springs and the nether springs.*
> -Judges 1:12-13, 15

Father, did you walk the Negev's wadis
before you gave them to my husband? The pathless dust,
stone and sand drinking the blood of afterbirth.

In spring, dead flowers rise in red skirts,
and you will wander south
to look your grandson in the eye.

My hair grows past my waist. I wanted life —
you gave water. And perhaps these are the same.
My husband will be gentle, or not, as he sees fit.

Each year, we thirst between the springs
you forgot to give me. Now they call me
greedy, discontent. My calves ache.

Clifftop convection burns the crest of my shoulders
as I plant the cord, draw the line taut: I am
more than the red tent, more than my circumcised son.

I am elusive as the evening blaze of grass. I return
like the wadi blooms, but each year I am smaller,
more brittle. The valley sun sets in colors I cannot name.

Sara Dallmayr
THE VULNERABILITY OF COMMON CARP

You appear to arrive somewhere, only to find yourself
back at the starting point. When I was a child perhaps
I understood this better, like when I would try to walk up
a sunbeam, through the window, into another ethereal
dimension. The shadows of Monday carried no weight
at all, for example. I knew that at once. Or how I once saw edges
of light along the top of a wall, and I was certain there was another
room on the other side, with familiar people I must know
the way a tree in the woods grows wide instead of tall.
Bands which encircle outward and we all brush into one another,
the bumpers of our timelines give us a jolt: *do I know you?*
It's not even the asking so much, and this is what I wanted to say,
is that my hands often feel like two fish, mouths open and eyes
a mask of nothing, a gulp for truth with a flash of silver lining.
Or a pair of mewling kittens with eyes yet not open, awake
but without vision, feeling in all the preeminent customs, asking
and knowing what they require in the time they can manipulate.
When I learned to fish, I always returned the fish to the lake,
until our neighbor came along one day and declared carp useless.
As children, we were forced to go about our business of play
with our game of jarts, while the carp writhed and flipped along
the shoreline. A lesson, I suppose, in the dangers of being perceived
as obsolete. Always be useful. Don't be a bottom feeder. Don't retain
the audacity to question the unseen which casts your fate.
The light was pale across the lake water, brown and raw and real
as the plunge of Michigan summer where we would tread water
in the green wave echoes under the dock, our faces lit with ripples.

I knew then the carp deserved to slip back into its source, not only
because our neighbor's perceptions were incorrect, but still, the heave
of fish against the beach, surrounded by oxygen in all the wrong ways.
We grew as tall as the reeds and the cattails and the tops of pontoons
until we could see for ourselves whose name the light called.
You appear to arrive somewhere, only to find yourself
back at the starting point. A child letting go. A fish in the air.

Hannah Boysko
JETTY

Sometimes we find ourselves in the sand, a flounder on the shore,
beached whale of exhaustion from swimming too far up the reef,
from trying to catch up to the current. I look to you, and I see a
sponge with everything running through it. I look at me and I see
a sponge that is wrung out and ready. It is funny to find myself
on another coin and so much drier. I still can't escape the waves,
but I think they might save me. A month ago I had been trapped
in a mountain of sand. Instead of kissing you, I kissed the shape
of your lips and wept that you would fade away. My endless
vibrations did not sound like me, or much of anything at all. And
then, the wave crashed and my legs bowed, knocked me from the
dunes away, my back on the ground, my back against your back.
Us both by the jetty, an ebb and flow of holding and tugging.
Swirling pools, my arms are a briny sea star trying to hold you.

Jerry Dennis
WAVES (A FOUND POEM)

What else is so inconstant, so *wavering*?
Wind. Candle flame. Lovetalk. Youth. Only a fool
would be out in that howl. The roar,
the shredded crests, the white tracers streaming
while the lethal breakers

curve their backs and crash. They could signify allegorical waves
or the many things that come in waves. Sound. Trouble
in our lives. The electro-magnetic spectrum from gamma ray
and x-ray to microwave and radio wave. The harmonies of gravity
in deep space, whorls of dust and gases spiraling among the stars.

They begin simply: A disturbance and a transfer of energy. They *are*
energy, passing through the body, visible only on the surface,
a flexing of muscles, ripples testing the cohesive force
of molecules on the surface. Capillary wave, wavelet, cat's
paw, gravity wave, chop, swell (a true sine curve), train of
breakers. Time rolls over us in long-period waves. They approach,
crest, pass, and in the troughs we get on with our lives. And then,
another crest.

The waves, she said, the clock. We run on sea-time, she said,
and laughed. There is nothing settled in this universe. All
is rippling, all is dancing. Isadora Duncan said
"My first idea of movement, of the dance, certainly came
from the rhythm of the waves."

Steep waves are unstable. In ordinary gravity waves
water swirls in defined orbits that remain in place
as energy passes through them. Weather fronts. Wind
on wheat fields. (My son, Aaron, age nine, watching grass-waves
billowing across a meadow said, "So *that's* what the wind
looks like.")

Labor contractions. Remorse. Fever. Spasms of orgasm (May Sarton:
"a spasmodic wave of union with the whole universe.")

Barbarian invaders. The electro-chemical surges
pulsing through our brains in sleep, like rollers
on an ocean. In physics a soliton
is a quantum or quasiparticle
propagated as a traveling nondissipative wave
neither preceded nor followed by another.

It is the same wave
throughout the world, the same wave
rolling, rising, bursting, thundering. A dreadful sight!

In 1861 a freak wave struck the Bishop Lighthouse
and smashed a fog bell a hundred feet above the rocks.
Conflicting forces raised the swell and it collapsed
in a spilling or surging breaker, the energy
carried for a thousand miles poised to explode
in a single shattering burst of spray.
See the whitecaps, feel the impact, hear the turmoil

like a thousand waterfalls. The wind meets them in a shock
of war, the chargers rear but go on and the wind blows back
their manes. Sea horses do men call such waves on every
coast of the world. Whitemaned seahorses champing,
purling, flowing, floating foampool, flower unfurling.

As they neared the shore they fell
in one long concussion, like a wall
falling. Muffled thuds like logs
falling. And in me too the wave rises, swells

O Death! The huge uproar
a world of sounds: hollow boomings
and heavy roarings, great water tumblings, whispers, grinding

undertone of stones. It is time beating
against the shore. The rise and boom, the velvet ticking. Man-

time, she said as the clock ticked. Sea-time, she said
as another wave crashed. It says everything
passes, everything changes. It says
we are utterly, beautifully,
momentary.

Sources:

The Odyssey, Homer (tr. Alexander Pope).
Cape Cod, Henry David Thoreau.
Ulysses, James Joyce.
The Waves, Virginia Woolf.
The Outermost House, Henry Beston.
The Narrow Road to the Deep North, Richard Flanagan.
The Windward Shore, The Bird in the Waterfall,
and author's notes, Jerry Dennis.

Hannah Boysko
LOVE POEM AT THE INTERTIDAL

I used to fall through waves and crash
into the wind.

Full. Ballooning.
Salt, current, jellyfish

stings, they were fog
and fire, like I was.

We were under water
when I loved you.

Skin dried, salt-stretched.
Could you tell yourself the truth

with this seaweed — my hair
over your lips? I never found out.

My tongue whirled laughter
into pearls, covered silence

in cold water. We buried hope
in the sand and called it

a holiday, or sometimes,
forever. Love

was its own cruelty.
At summer's end,

I walked ashore at low tide.
Saw a place to stand

in the sun, stay.

Moira Walsh
WHAT TO DO IF YOU ARE SWEPT AWAY

Water
of its own accord
never flows straight

The riptide will not carry you
clear to nowhere

At some intrinsic limit
it will curve
ever so gradually
back to shore

Depositing you
on the same beach

Although
of course
not the same

Kenneth Jakubas

PARABLE ON BEAVER ISLAND

for Lake Geneserath

It's hard to stay afloat and pee,
harder still fishing a pole
from the water of a lonely lake.
That lake loves the taste of mistakes,
though it still swallows them whole.

When all is backwards,
you find the monster
that got away & make him
swallow your mistakes.
The life you left behind

is over water. It's hard to stay afloat
& pee without a noodle between your legs
or a generous captain to steer you to shore.
Later on, you'll pile into a van
& find it difficult to find the road

that leads to the edge of life,
a hard to find circle of stones & sage
in line with the midsummer solstice,
placed before time had a name for the people
who carved bowls into the stones.

It's hard to beg an offering from the orifice
of a thing too old to touch, monster too big
to catch, birch tree whose fat limb we sit on
like artists in a new school. It shouldn't be
so hard to leave a thing behind.

What's behind you is out of sight,
& below you is the dark.
From an airplane you are an island,
afloat at the edge of life itself,
letting go of what's behind you.

Nathan Manley
LITTLE SONG OF SUNSET

Her unearthly ember, flaked from the forge
some dire and dutiful angel has struck
beyond this vast animal of cloud, once
gravid with rain, now spent, empty-headed
and listless as a Deist's god. But for
this color our language lacks—this orange
of neither fruit nor flame, but blazing still
as if its atoms strove for holiness,
failing short of it and falling, meanwhile,
among pond flowers, these unlistening,
tasseled ears of corn asleep in their rows,
tucked in the summer's tree-lit distances—
you might have known it: that this is the world
at its speechless remove. All this, the world.

Ellen Lord
BLUES

after Leonard Cohen (1972)

You provide the music
if you want to live here.
Do you like this poem?
I wrote it in a heartache
I can no longer recall.
Do you remember when we met?
I did not know then
that you could dance.
It would have made all the difference.

CONTRIBUTOR BIOS

HOLLY EVA ALLEN is a writer currently living in California. She is working on a Master's in English at Claremont Graduate University. Her work has been previously published with *Rue Scribe, Blue Unicorn, Funicular,* and *Sand Hills.* You can find her work at hollyevaallen.wordpress.com.

DIANA ARNOLD is a New York City poet and performer who attempts to distill the small moments of clarity in our lives. Her published poems "Wraparound," "History," "Both the Path," and "Laundry Day" can be found online and in her first poetry collection *If/When,* while her original show *On the Table* can be seen live at Dixon Place next year and streaming soon.

MARTIN ARNOLD has published poems in many fine journals, including *Crazyhorse, Carolina Quarterly,* and *Best New Poets 2012.* His first chapbook, *A Million Distant Glittering Catastrophes,* won the 2009-2010 Pavement Saw Chapbook contest. *Earthquake Owner's Manual* won the 2013 Unicorn Press First Book Award. His most recent chapbook, *Promiscuous Beauty,* was published in 2019 by Finishing Line Press.

When not teaching, DEVON BALWIT sets her hand to the plough and chases chickens in Portland, OR. Her most recent chapbook is *Rubbing Shoulders with the Greats* (Seven Kitchens Press, 2020). Her most recent collection, *Dog-Walking in the Shadow of Pyongyang,* is forthcoming (Nixes Mate Press, 2021). For more regarding her work, visit her website: https://pelapdx.wixsite.com/devonbalwitpoet.

ANDREW BAN is a sixth-grader attending Seoul International School in South Korea. He loves writing in his free time, and his other hobbies include playing tennis and skateboarding.

HANNAH BOYSKO is a writer, performer, and educator living in Brooklyn, NY. She creates urban farming programs for kids and is learning to care for chickens, bees, and her houseplants. One day, she would just love to bike to the beach with you.

ANA CABALLERO is happiest drinking coffee and writing at dawn, before her two kids, husband, and inbox wake up. What she writes can be found online at www.anamariacaballero.com.

DAVID CAPPS is a philosophy professor at Western Connecticut State University. He is the author of three chapbooks: *Poems from the First Voyage* (The Nasiona Press, 2019), *A Non-Grecian Non-Urn* (Yavanika Press, 2019), and *Colossi* (Kelsay Books, 2020). His manuscript, *Drawn in Evening Light,* was a finalist for the 2020 Gasher first book scholarship. He lives in New Haven, CT.

LEAH FRANCESCA CHRISTIANSON's work has appeared or is forthcoming in *Split Lip Magazine, Bending Genres, TriQuarterly, River Teeth,* and other publications. She earned her MFA from Miami University, where she was editor-in-chief of

Oxford Magazine. She recently completed a novel and is working on a book of hybrid nonfiction.

LAUREN CLAUS is a medical student at Johns Hopkins University. Her poems are forthcoming or have recently appeared in *The Journal of the American Medical Association (JAMA)*, *Hawaii Pacific Review*, *Tipton Poetry Review*, *Zone 3*, and *Briar Cliff Review*, among other publications.

*SARA DALLMAYR is originally from Kalamazoo, Michigan, where she attended Western Michigan University. Dallmayr's work has recently appeared or is forthcoming in *Eclectica*, *Texas Literary Review*, *Third Coast*, *High Shelf Press*, *SWWIM*, *3Elements*, *Penn Review*, and others. She currently lives in South Bend, Indiana with her husband and two cats. Dallmayr works for the post office as a rural carrier. Her favorite pastimes include collecting incense and eating pasties in Hell.

*JERRY DENNIS earns his living writing nonfiction books (*The Living Great Lakes*, *The Windward Shore*, etc.). His poetry and brief prose have appeared recently in *PANK*, *Michigan Quarterly Review*, *Right Hand Pointing*, *New World Writing*, and elsewhere. He lives with artist Gail Dennis in northern Michigan. His website is www.jerrydennis.net.

Born in Georgia, raised in Michigan, *SCOTT DORSCH is an MFA fiction candidate at the University of Idaho, where he is a Writing in the Wild Fellow. His work has appeared in *The Midwestern Gothic* and is forthcoming in *Everything Change: A Climate Fiction Anthology*, vol. III. He is the former fiction editor for *Fugue* and a recipient of a 2021 Good Hart Artist Residency. He is at work on his first novel and short story collection. Follow his work or get in touch at scottdorsch.com.

AMANDA GANUS is an MFA student at George Mason University. A native of Lubbock, Texas, she now lives in Fairfax, Virginia with her cat, Augustus. When Amanda isn't working, she enjoys museums, cooking, and watching too much reality television with her partner. Occasionally, these activities are interspersed with writing.

BRIAN GATZ lives and works in Illinois.

*KEITH GRIMES is a husband of one, a father of two, and an owner of three. When he's not working as a writer or reading very long books, you'll probably find him watching entirely too much Netflix.

*KENNETH JAKUBAS holds an MFA from Western Michigan University, where he served as poetry editor for *Third Coast*. His poetry and prose has appeared or is forthcoming in *RHINO*, *Passages North*, and *Birdcoat Quarterly*, among others. He is currently at work on a mini-series for the website shitlitfic.com.

AVERY K. JAMES is a poetry MFA student at Georgia College and State University and works as a staff reader for the *Arts & Letters* literary magazine. Her work has been published or is forthcoming in places such as *Forum*, *Southern Humanities Review*, *Hey I'm Alive Magazine*, and *QA Poetry*.

*ELLEN LORD is a Michigan native. Her writing has appeared in *Walloon Writers Review, r.kv.r.y Quarterly Literary Journal, Open Palm Print*, Poets Society of Michigan/Peninsula Poets chapbooks and TDAL Poets Night Out chapbooks. She won the Landmark Books Haiku Contest in 2017 and 2019. She is a behavioral health therapist.

NATHAN MANLEY is the author of two chapbooks, *Numina Loci* (Mighty Rogue Press, 2018) and *Ecology of the Afterlife* (Split Rock Press, 2021). His poems have appeared or are forthcoming in *Think, Natural Bridge, Spillway, Split Rock Review, Puerto del Sol, Crab Creek Review* and others.

HANNAH MARSHALL lives and works in Illinois. Marshall's poem "This Is a Love Poem to Trees" will appear in *The Best American Poetry 2021*. Her poems can also be found in *Poetry Daily, New Ohio Review, The South Carolina Review*, and elsewhere. Marshall holds an MFA from Converse College.

THERESA MONTEIRO lives in New Hampshire with her husband and six children. She is a former teacher and holds an MFA from the University of New Hampshire. She has had poems published in *The American Journal of Poetry, River Heron Review, Pittsburgh Poetry Journal, Tipton Poetry Journal, Black Fork Review, Good Fat Poetry, Silver Needle Press*, and forthcoming in *The Meadow* and *Presence*. She received the Dick Shea Memorial Prize for poetry in 2019.

*NANCY ADAMS NASH, the artist whose work is featured on the cover, lives in Charlevoix, Michigan.

JOHN NIEBUHR is a solar energy director, lyricist, and a creative writing instructor at Burbank Adult School. His writing has appeared in *Hash Journal, Allegory Ridge, MMPP*, and other small presses.

RISA PAPPAS is a poet, filmmaker, editor, narrator, and pro wrestling ring announcer. Her recent publications include the *Placeholder Press, Entropy*, and *bluntly magazine*. Risa is Editor-in-Chief at Tolsun Books and earned her MFA in creative writing from Fairleigh Dickinson University. She resides near Philadelphia.

SUPHIL LEE PARK is the author of *Present Tense Complex*, winner of the Marystina Santiestevan Prize, forthcoming in 2021. She grew up in South Korea and graduated from New York University with a BA in English and from the University of Texas at Austin with an MFA in Poetry. You can find more about her at: https://suphil-lee-park.com.

HEATHER QUINN is a poet and artist who lives in awe of the creative spirit. She was a finalist in *House Mountain Review*'s 2019 Broadside Contest, a semi-finalist in *Cutthroat*'s 2020 Joy Harjo's Poetry Prize, a semi-finalist in *Prometheus Dreaming*'s 2019 Unbound Competition, and was featured in *Palette Poetry*'s "Poetry We Admire." Her website is heatherquinnpoet.com.

BRUCE ROBINSON shuttles between Brooklyn and Albany, NY, Recent work appears or is forthcoming in *Pangyrus, Maintenant, Evening Street Review, Main Street Rag*, and *Spoon River Poetry Review*.

BRETT THOMPSON has been writing poetry since his graduate days at the University of New Hampshire where he earned an M.A. in English Writing with a concentration in poetry. He has been published in various journals, including *Plainsongs, Tilde, District Lit, The Literary Nest*, and the *Cobalt Review*. He teaches and lives in New Hampshire with his wife and two young daughters.

BILLY THRASHER is a poet and graduate of the MFA program at Lindenwood University. The simple, brief moments in life catch his attention and spark his creativity. He has poems published in *Moon Magazine, Lagom: A Journal, Jenny, Dovecote, Panoplyzine, White Wall*, and *As You Were: The Military Review*.

IAIN TWIDDY studied literature at university and lived for several years in northern Japan. His poetry has appeared in *Harvard Review, The Common, Salamander, Illuminations, The Blue Mountain Review, The Stinging Fly, The London Magazine*, and elsewhere.

*Michigan-born MOIRA WALSH has lived on three continents and is currently based in Germany, where she writes and translates. She became a published poet in 2020. Moira is the 2021 Anne-Marie Oomen Fellow at Poetry Forge and was a Thomas Lux Scholar at the 2021 Palm Beach Poetry Festival. Her website is https://linktr.ee/moira_walsh.

ANTHONY WARNKE'S poetry has appeared in *Cimarron Review, North American Review, Sentence, Sixth Finch*, and *Sugar House Review*, among other publications. He teaches writing at Green River College and lives in Seattle.

*CAIT WEST is in book publishing in Grand Rapids, Michigan, where she lives with her husband and cat. Her publications include fiction in *Nota Bene* and *Old Northwest Review* and creative nonfiction in the *3288 Review*. She writes about her journey out of the stay-at-home-daughter movement at caitwest.com.

MARCUS WHALBRING'S third collection of poems is forthcoming from Milk & Cake Press. His poems have appeared in *The Cortland Review, Spry, Underwood Press* and others. He earned his MFA from Miami University. He's a father, husband, and teacher.

ERIN WILSON'S poems have appeared or are forthcoming in *Salamander Magazine, Crab Creek Review, takahē, The Prairie Journal, A Magazine of Canadian Literature, Pembroke Magazine, Hamilton Stone Review, Under a Warm Green Linden, The Honest Ulsterman*, and elsewhere. Her first collection is *At Home with Disquiet*. She lives and writes in a small town in northern Ontario, Canada.

READER BIOS

*PETER BOISVERT is a native Detroiter who now lives, works, and writes in Ann Arbor. He pays the bills writing code, writes poems and stories in between, is a graduate of Pacific University's MFA program, still prefers to sit in the dark in an actual movie theater and cry when the hero comes back for the kid, and one year inspected and certified all the rubber life rafts carried on the sailboats running in the Port Huron to Mackinaw race.

*KELLI FITZPATRICK is an author and editor from Michigan. Her fiction has been published by Simon and Schuster, *Flash Fiction Online*, and Crazy 8 Press, among others, and her poetry appears in *Dunes Review*, *Still Life*, and *KYSO Flash*. Currently, she writes and edits for the *Star Trek Adventures* game line from Modiphius. She is an advocate of the arts, public education, and gender rights and representation. Connect at KelliFitzpatrick.com and on Twitter @KelliFitzWrites.

*TERESA SCOLLON is the author of the poetry collection *To Embroider the Ground with Prayer* (Wayne State University Press). Her essay was included in *Elemental*, an anthology of Michigan essayists. She is a National Endowment for the Arts fellow and won the 2018 Moveen Poetry Prize. She teaches the Front Street Writers program at the TBAISD Career-Tech Center.

*When EMMA SMITH was in middle school, teachers said she was having difficulty reading. As her worried parents contemplated purchasing Hooked on Phonics, Emma picked up *IT* by Stephen King and hasn't slowed down since. She loves to read everything from sci fi/fantasy to oudated anarchist literature to the classics. You can find Emma working with animals, reading books, or hiking with friends.

*JENNIFER YEATTS' literary life has included MA and MFA degrees in poetry, teaching writing in various forms, and editorial roles at *Passages North* and *Fugue*. She is the director of coffee for Higher Grounds Trading Company.

*denotes Michigan native or resident

Call for Patrons

Dunes Review is a not-for-profit endeavor to promote creative work within the Northern Michigan writing community and beyond.

The cost of publication can be underwritten in part by individual contributions. We invite you to support the publication of the next issue with a donation of $25.

Send your check payable to **Michigan Writers** to:

Michigan Writers

P.O. Box 2355

Traverse City, MI 49685

Thank you in advance for your support!

SUBMISSION GUIDELINES

Dunes Review welcomes work from writers, artists, and photographers at all stages of their careers living anywhere in the world, though we particularly love featuring writers with ties to Michigan and the Midwest. We are open to all styles and aesthetics, but please read the following paragraph carefully to dive a little deeper into what we're looking for.

Ultimately, we're looking for work that draws us in from the very first line: with image, with sound, with sense, with lack of sense. We're looking for writing that makes us *feel* and bowls us over, lifts us up, and takes us places we've never been to show us ordinary things in ways we've never seen them. We're looking for poems and stories and essays that teach us how to read them and pull us back to their beginnings as soon as we've read their final lines. We're looking for things we can't wait to read again, things we can't wait to share with the nearest person who will listen. Send us your best work. We'll give it our best attention.

Submissions are accepted only via our Submittable platform: www.dunesreview.submittable.com. We do not consider work sent through postal mail or email. Any submissions sent through email will not be read or responded to. Please see further guidelines posted on our site. We look forward to reading your work!

Made in the USA
Monee, IL
17 April 2021